Skate Ra

Written by Hannah Reed

Photography by Michael Curtain

alphakids

My name is Cody.
I am ten years old.
I am a skate racer.

2

I started skating with an old pair
of roller skates in my backyard.
When I started I wasn't very good
but then I started to get better.

So my mother bought me a pair
of in-line skates and took me
to the skating rink.

I liked skating at the skating rink because
I could go faster than in my backyard.

The coach of the skating team saw
me skating one day.

"I think you could be a good skate racer,"
he said.

So I started training.

Training was fun.

I learned how to be a skate racer.

I learned how to fall over safely.

I also learned how to start quickly.

After a few weeks I was ready to start racing.

My mother helped me to get ready
for my first race.
She showed me how to clean
all the parts of my skates.
Clean skates help you
to skate faster.

I put on my helmet
and my racing suit.

Now I was ready
to race.

I was very scared but it was really good fun.

I didn't win because I was too scared to pass other people in the race.

I had to learn to pass other people.

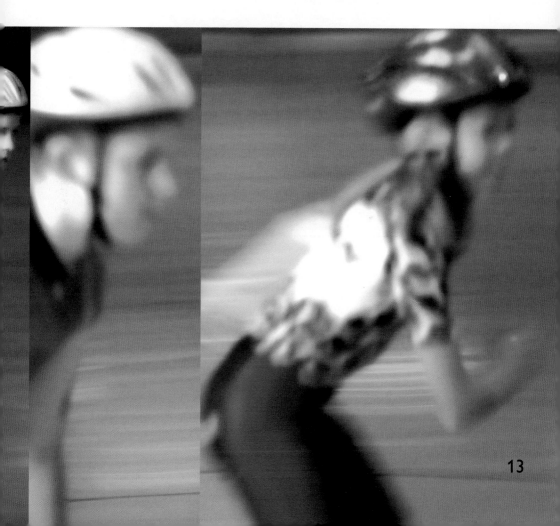

I worked really hard and I got
better and better at racing.
I started to win lots and lots of races.

Last year I came second
in the skate racing championships.

I like skate racing. I like going fast
and I like winning races. And I like
the friends I make while I'm racing.